THE
WARRIOR
PRINCESS 1

: SIKH WOMEN IN BATTLE

Stories And Poems About
Sikh Women Saint-Warriors

SACHA SAUDA
GURMAT PARCHAR SOCIETY
2575 STEELES AVENUE EAST, UNIT No 18.
BRAMPTON, ONT. L6T 5TI CANADA
TEL. : (905) 459-8351
FAX : (905) 459-5986

Written by Harjit Singh

Illustrated by Harjit Singh "Artist"

Designed by Taranjit Singh

© Harjit Singh
All rights reserved

First Edition Published Aug 2001
Second Editon Published Dec 2001

No part of this book may be reproduced in
any manner without written permission.

Can be had from:
B. Chattar Singh Jiwan Singh
Bazar Mai Sewan, Amritsa (India)
Tele : 91-183-2542346, 2545973
ISBN 1-903863-007
Price : Rs.100/-

Published by www.Sikh-Heroes.com
Email: Harjit@sikh-heroes.com

Printed and Bound in India by
B. Chattar Singh Jiwan Singh (Exports)
Bazar Mai Sewan, Amritsar (India)
Tele : 0183-542346   Fax : 0183-557973
E-Mail : csjs@jla.vsnl.net.in

DEDICATION

*To my parents for inspiring me
with Sikh stories as I was growing up.*

CONTENTS

Women have been treated as second class citizens for thousands of years. The founder of Sikhism, Guru Nanak Dev strived to change that by educating the masses. He wrote :

"So why call her bad?
From her, kings are born.

From woman, woman is born;
without woman, there would be no one at all.

Nanak:
only the True Lord
is without a woman.
That mouth which praises
the Lord continually
is blessed and beautiful.

Nanak:
those faces shall be radiant
in the Court of the True Lord."

Guru Granth Sahib, 473

WHERE IN THE WORLD?

The stories in this book are set in 18th Century Punjab - "The Land of the Five Rivers". They are stories of ordinary people living in extraordinary times. About people like you and me who struggled for survival.

These people were the Sikhs. Neither Hindus nor Muslims they were inspired by Guru Gobind Singh - the Protector sent from God. The Sikhs that stood up to injustice were known as the Khalsa Army. These mighty saint-warriors, both men and women, roamed Punjab determined to carry on the mission of Guru Gobind Singh and uproot the unwanted Mughal invaders.

Punjab at that time was much bigger than it is now. The Punjab of today is split between India and Pakistan.

LIONESS

Based on a true story

The wild animals were howling in the nearby jungle. The wind was biting Ranjit Kaur's face as she wrapped her midnight-blue shawl around a little tighter. Nothing to be afraid of, she quietly carried on repeating God's name, "Waheguru, Waheguru" in time to her steps. It protected her in a glove of spiritual love.

She looked through the trees at the magnificent setting sun, for a moment she forgot all about the war and was lost in the magic and mystery of the Creator. She felt as beautiful as a blossoming flower radiating love and life in all directions.

"Sister! Sister!"

Ranjit Kaur quickly turned around and saw a young boy in the uniform of the Khalsa warrior. He was wearing the blue battledress. A long curved sword hung down his left side, chain-mail armour across his chest and a three metal discuses around his blue pointed turban. Ranjit Kaur greeted him, "Waheguru Jee Ka Khalsa, Waheguru Jee Kee Fateh! Gurmukh

Singh. Why are you out so late?"

"I was about to ask you the same thing sister. Don't you know how dangerous it is for a woman to be out her alone while there are Mughal soldiers patrolling the area? You better have a good excuse, otherwise I'm marching you right back to the camp."

"Gurmukh Singh, don't worry about me. Our leader, the Jathedar, has asked me to fetch some important news from the village chief."

"But you know the war for our independence is at it's peak and there's trouble around every corner. Look, I've got an idea - it's safer for you to go back to the lake and rejoin the Khalsa Army and I will go in your place."

"Why do you think it's any safer for you to go, Gurmukh Singh?"

"It will be dark soon and I don't think it's right for a woman to go anywhere alone. I am a Khalsa warrior, I carry five weapons and I am prepared to die fighting. I want people to remember me by telling stories about how brave I was."

Just then a bat came flying out of the dark trees directly towards Gurmukh Singh, he didn't know what was attacking him and screaming loudly he covered his face with his hands!

Ranjit Kaur burst out laughing, "You're not so brave now little brother! You should remember that I too have been blessed with the Guru's amrit-nectar. I too carry a long sword over my blue battledress and wear a warrior's turban. God is always with me. But you my younger brother have much to learn about showing off and are probably at more risk than me!"

"I insist on going with you sister."

"Look brother you are wasting valuable time. I'll give you five seconds to turn around and run all the way home."

Gurmukh Singh stood defiantly looking Ranjit Kaur directly in the eye.

"I'm going to grab you by the ear, drag you

home and after the Khalsa has finished their evening prayers, I'm going to tell them the story of the great Gurmukh Singh and the black bat!"

"OK, OK I'm going, but be careful."

Gurmukh Singh ran down the path towards the lake while Ranjit Kaur continued her journey towards the village.

Gurmukh Singh's fears were not unfounded. Small bands of Mughal soldiers were wandering around the lake seeking information about the Sikhs. Every Sikh was aware of this. However, it did not deter Ranjit Kaur. She fearlessly went on her way to the village. She had absolute faith in God and her blessed sword. She reached the village chief's house. His mother and wife came out and hugged her, "O Ranjit Kaur it's so good to see you again, God keeps you well."

It was getting late and they insisted that she spent the night with them. But before any arrangements were made the Chief entered the room and handed over the scroll. His grave expression brought total silence to the room.

What she read spelled disaster for the Khalsa. A large number of Ahmed Shah Abdali's troops were on their way to seize the Kahnuwaan Lake and the scroll contained orders to the Chief to help the troops.

"I must leave at once to warn the others. The Khalsa is at your service Chief - you are a brave man to have helped us."

Securing the scroll inside her pouch, she covered herself with her shawl and headed back to the Kahnuwaan Lake. One of the women tried to make her stay saying, "It's too late for your Khalsa, just save yourself Ranjit - don't go back." But to Ranjit Kaur, life was not worth anything without her Khalsa family.

By now it was midnight. The skies were clear and the moonlight lit up the earth. In this calm and still atmosphere, Ranjit Kaur reached the outskirts of the quiet village and walked as fast as possible towards the lake. She had about three miles to cover. She increased her pace and marched with determination through the sounds of howling animals. She quietly carried on repeating God's Name, "Waheguru, Waheguru" in time to her footsteps and felt protected.

Two Mughal soldiers with swords in their waist-bands, rode past her left side.

The heavenly moonlight glowed from Ranjit Kaur's angelic face and intensified her beauty. The soldiers suddenly pulled their horses across her path and quickly dismounting they tried to grab her hands. She darted away with lightning speed and threatened them, "There will be trouble if you touch me!"

She fearlessly looked at the soldiers and under-neath her shawl she grabbed the handle of her sword, just in case, "Who are you soldiers and what do you want?"

"We are commanders of the royal forces young lady."

"Then what business do you have with me?"

Without answering, the second soldier shouted, "Who are you? And where are you wandering to at this time of night?"

"Whoever I may be, you have no right to question me."

Saying this Ranjit Kaur tried to walk briskly past them. The first soldier quickly moved to block her way once again, "We have orders to find out where the Sikhs are hiding. You look like a Sikh so until you explain what you are doing we aren't going to let you go anywhere."

"That's right, I am a Sikh, what are you going to do about it?"

"Then consider yourself under arrest!" said the first soldier.

He looked at the other one and loudly said, "I think you better grab her and put her on your horse, because I don't know what I'll do if I get too close to her."

Both looked at Ranjit Kaur's face and then looked at each other and started laughing. Ranjit Kaur looked at them like a hungry lioness at a couple of sheep. Her eyes were red with anger.

There was a brief silence before the first soldier calmly spoke again, "Pretty lady, we have been sent to find the Sikhs. However, we are not animals. We are human. We too have pumping hearts in our chest. What kind of heart would it be that does not worship a beautiful angel like you."

Both men were intoxicated with Ranjit Kaur's beauty. A mere glimpse of her face had injected lustful insanity into them. Ranjit Kaur stared at their faces but remained silent. The other soldier continued, "What are you going to get from living on the run and hiding in the jungles with the Sikhs. Come with us. You can wear fine silk and live like a Queen. You can even choose which one of us you want to marry!"

Ranjit Kaur silently stared at the soldiers. She had made her decision to continue or to die fighting. But her silence was misinterpreted. The first soldier lunged forward trying in vain to grab her wrist, "Come, sit on my horse. It is

17

getting late my love."

Ranjit Kaur moved swiftly, taking two steps backward she drew her sword from under her shawl. It flashed like lightning under the moonlight.

"COME ANY CLOSER AND I WILL NOT BE RESPONSIBLE FOR WHAT HAPPENS!"

The soldiers burst out laughing.

"An angel drawing a sword! That's a first!"

The other soldier added, "Isn't she beautiful when she's angry?"

The first soldier had never seen a woman protect her honour like a lioness, but she was still only a woman. He tried to grab her with his outstretched arms. A flashing sword dazzled him and he screamed in agony as his left hand dropped to the ground.

Having been bitten by the lioness both soldiers drew their swords and charged towards her.

Ranjit Kaur lunged forward at the first soldier again and cut off his sword hand. He retreated squirming in pain.

The other soldier was a skilled swordsman. His continuous attacks inflicted several wounds to Ranjit Kaur. Blood covered her whole face. Exhaustion was setting in.

Suddenly, the strength of the Guru's amrit-nectar injected so much courage into her, that she forgot all about her wounds and pains.

Yelling the battle cry, "BOLAY SO NIHAL, SAT SREE AKAL," her sword moved with such force that the soldier's head dropped to the ground and landed with a thud. His body fell in a heap next to it.

Ranjit Kaur quickly looked around for the first soldier, but he had escaped without trace. Totally exhausted she still managed to search the heaped body and found several papers in the dead soldier's pockets. Seizing them, she mounted his horse and rode home to the Kahnuwaan Lake.

Ranjit Kaur fighting soldiers in the forest

As she approached the camp she mustered up every last ounce of energy and yelled, 'JATHEDAR! JATHEDAR!'

The Jathedar, several Khalsa warriors and little Gurmukh Singh came running out to meet her. Seeing her blood red face and exhausted condition they carried her inside. Little Gurmukh Singh started crying.

Ranjit Kaur's sisters wiped her face and cleaned her wounds while she searched her pouch and handed the papers over to the Jathedar. He was amazed to find full details of the Mughal's battle plans.

Ranjit Kaur was honoured greatly by the Khalsa, God's kindness had given her the courage to fight her attackers and to save her Khalsa family from a bloody massacre.

News of Ranjit Kaur's courage spread through out the Khalsa Panth - the Sikh Nation. She became known as the "Brave Daughter of the Guru"

FIGHTING SPIRIT

A fictional poem based on the small groups of Khalsa that rescued kidnapped women.

BACKGROUND

In 1739, the Persian ruler Nadir Shah marched via Afghanistan to rob India. His armies stormed through Punjab. They savagely burnt down everything that came in their way and massacred thousands of innocent people.

Having amassed an enormous booty and a large number of kidnapped women, they headed back home through Punjab. But, this time the Khalsa was waiting for them. They were hiding in the thick forests on the banks of the River Ravi.

It was the hot month of May and the army marched slowly, so the Khalsa pounced on them time and time again. They took them by surprise and rescued the women and treasures.

Nadir Shah asked the Govenor Zakriya Khan, "Who are these barbarians?" Zakriya replied, "They are a group founded by Guru Nanak who visit their sacred Amritsar twice a year and then disappear." Nadir Shah then warned the Govenor, "It wont be long before they rule this land of yours!"

****

After Guru Gobind Singh the Khalsa had a price on their head in their own homeland. They were forced to live on the run in jungles. But, they never shirked their responsibility - they were the police force, they were law and justice - they were God's Army blessed by Guru Gobind Singh himself...

Awesome warriors
that pounce like panthers,
on mighty battle horses
against Persian Forces.

An invisible breeze
through the jungle trees,
roar like thunder :
God's Army - Perfect Khalsa!

Khalsa-Spy in orange,
blue and black,
camouflaged, she follows
the Army's track.

Crawling under bushes
like a venomous snake,
perching like a hawk
beside the lake.

Hidden in a rock-cave
small and compact,
it'll soon be time,
time to attack!

Around the river
like a poisonous snake,
towards the tents -
she'll make them quake.

Slips by the guards
on her silent feet,
sings "Waheguru"
with each heartbeat.

Khalsa-Spy looking across the river at the tents

Quick look left
and a sharp look back,
it'll soon be time,
time to attack!

Eagle-eyed she finds
the Punjabi pearls,
her kidnapped sisters
are now slave-girls.

Chained together
inside a dirty tent,
soon to be owned
by a so called gent.

In Afghanistan
she'll be up for sale,
sold as a slave
to some arrogant male.

Each kidnapped woman
fears one thing:
her forced marriage
to a Muslim.

Khalsa spy
quickly scuttles around,
sketching a map
of the enemy's ground.

She disappears
like a passing breeze,
the Persians think
it's just rustling leaves.

By the Guru's grace
she'll be back,
back when it's time,
time to attack!

Mighty Persians
fought long and hard today,
against innocent farmers
stacking their hay.

Majestic Persians
say its good for their soul,
to slay parents and
watch their children groan.

Their village was eaten
by a monster's desire,
the wild orange animal
of the army's fire.

Handsome Persians
were so brave and strong,
they raped young girls -
it didn't seem wrong.

After a hard days work
they sleep nice and warm,
unaware of the
rising Khalsa storm.

Inside the tent where
the prisoners are kept,
beside the sisters
who've wept and wept.

Stands Princess Kaur
with a saintly face,
with her eyes closed
in a spiritual place:

"Dear Guru we are
your innocent children,
Merciful Master
grant us freedom.

Save us from
this sordid mess,
O Perfect Protector
of the Powerless.

Honour and cherish
Your daughter's right,
O Ocean of Love
and Unknowable Light.

Bless us with Waheguru's
Name and might,
break our chains,
make us stand and fight.

Invincible Power
no one knows your limit,
bless us now
with Your Fighting Spirit!"

The Persians yawn
at the crack of dawn,
their blood stained clothes
are still battle torn.

They pray a little
if they pray at all,
swearing and pushing
they walk real tall.

They reek of B.O.
and have stinking breath,
but that wont be enough
to scare away Death!

The Khalsa storm
is almost upon their land,
the Goddess of Death
is in the Khalsa's hand.

Guru Gobind Singh
no one knows Your limit,
the Khalsa is blessed
with Your Fighting Spirit!

The Khalsa is beautiful,
the Khalsa is bright,
the Khalsa protects
and does what's right.

Looking like mountains,
roaring like thunder,
riding on the wind
singing "God of Wonder!"

Across the rivers
and through the valleys,
chasing the Persians
like a swarm of bees.

Khalsa-Spy made
them a detailed map,
the Persian army will
fall into a deadly trap.

Hiding in the jungle
by the well walked track,
waiting for the time,
time to attack!

Khalsa-Spy, big,
brave and strong,
leads the way
singing her song.

Rides on her own
into the track,
face to face
with the Persian pack.

The Persian dogs
chase this Khalsa rabbit,
she charges at them
full of fighting spirit.

Tall blue turbans appear
from deep dark places,
the Persians are surrounded
by Khalsa faces!

No place to run now,
no place to hide,
Goddess of Death
slashes Persian pride.

Smashed falling heads
land with a thud,
the jungle ground
soaks up their blood.

The Persians lived
by their sinning culture,
they're only good
for a hungry vulture!

Sweet Princess Kaur
with her saintly face,
thanks Guru jee
for his merciful grace,

Guru Gobind Singh Jee
no one knows your limit,
The Khalsa is blessed
with Your

Fighting Spirit!

HEROIC NURSE

Based on a historical battle that took place in early 1823. The location was Nowshera, now in the Northern Province of Pakistan.

The green hills were soaked in blood. The powerful Afgan Army defended the hill top against a small troop of fearless Akali soldiers. The Afgan Army heavily outnumbered the Akalis - the bravest battalion of the Khalsa Army. But, these warrior lions of Guru Gobind Singh did not lose faith. They were united, like the waves in the ocean, by their deep blue battledress and turbans. They fought against the odds and faced the rain of enemy bullets, stones and arrows. Hacking their way through treacherous terrain, they hammered their way up the hill.

Time was running out for the Akalis. Maharaja Ranjit Singh had not arrived with reinforcements. The Afgans had won the support of thousands of local Muslims by distributing pamphlets that declared this battle as a holy war against Islam. The Akalis belonged to Akal, the Immortal God, and with Akal on their side who should they be afraid of? Being outnumbered did not scare them. Guru Gobind Singh had transformed them with his 'amrit' - the initiation nectar prepared in the indestructible iron bowl and stirred by the most awesome of weapons - the double-edged Khanda sword.

The words of their Guru father rang in their ears, "I will make one fight against 125,000, then and only then can I be called Gobind Singh!" The Akalis belonged to Akal, they fought for their Guru's honour and their only hope in life was to die fighting courageously on the battlefield.

The future of the Sikh Kingdom, the Khalsa Raj, depended on this battle. The Akalis marched forward led by the courageous warrior Akali Phoola Singh. The sun reflected like bolts of lightning from the sharp blades going around his mountain peaked turban. Raising his sword his thundering voice gave power to the battle cry, "BOLEH SO NIHAL." Every single Khalsa lion roared the response, "SAT SREE AKAL."

The Akali's spirits rose, new life was injected into them with each battle cry. They faced the Afgans with rejuvenated spirits, just seeing the fire in Akali Phoola Singh's eyes was enough to send the Afgans running in all directions.

Advancing into an almost deserted battlefield the Akalis had captured the hill top.

But then, from out of nowhere, bullets and arrows started raining down on the Akalis, the Afgans had hidden in hill caves and now charged out. Surrounding the Akalis they bombarded them with bullets and arrows. Akali Phoola Singh took a bullet in the chest and the mighty lion fell. The great warrior Karnail Singh Bania also fell wounded by another bullet. The Akalis wanted to die fighting, but seeing their leader's serious condition they decided it was wiser to retreat. The Afgans chased them down to the foothills.

The wounded were carried for about a mile, they marched passed their ammunition depot and reached the camp hospital. A few young Khalsa women busily nursed the wounded lions. Looking towards the hill they saw the enemy forces charging down like an avalanche. The Khalsa nurses along with the remaining Akali warriors, gathered their wounded and once again retreated to a safer location.

The mighty warrior Akali Phoola Singh

The Afgans were exhilarated by the fact that victory was almost in their ruthless hands. They marched triumphantly towards the deserted Akali camp. Reaching the undefended depot they desperately needed to find a mountain load of ammunition. Most of their army did not have rifles and without them they knew they stood no chance against the Khalsa Army reinforcements that were rapidly riding to the battle scene. On finding thousands of rifles, their joy had no bounds and the skies reverberated with their war cries.

Each soldier eagerly seized a weapon, but their hearts sunk down to the lowest depths of hell when they realised there were no bullets. Searching frantically, they ripped apart every storage tent and overturned every stack of crates. Like thirsty men in the desert they ran in all directions looking for even a tiny clue as to where the metal messengers of death could be. Finally, they located crate after crate full to the brim with the finest bullets stuffed full of gunpowder. Once again their joy had no bounds and the valleys echoed with their cheers.

Surrounded by a sea of ammunition the Afgan Army danced like drunken men waving their new found guns in the air. Without warning, an incredible explosion suddenly shocked the sky and shook the mountains. Flames shot up hundreds of feet into the sky, like an erupting volcano spewing out its insides with all the force and fury of ten thousand angry gods. Bodies went flying in all directions like fragile rag dolls. Within a blink of an eye, the Afgans dancing heaven had turned them into black logs of charcoal feeding the flames of hell on earth.

By now, the Lion Of Punjab - Shera Punjab, Maharaja Ranjit Singh, had crossed the Attock river. He appeared on the horizon like the light of the rising sun after a dark and stormy night, the rays of hope reached out in all directions in the form of Khalsa warrior after Khalsa warrior. Whether riding on horseback or marching on foot, each battalion was led by the flag bearers waving the Khalsa flags high in the sky.

They whispered "Waheguru, Waheguru" with each breath, their secret power given to them when they were blessed with Amrit.

43

General Hari Singh Naluwa commanded them and they rode like the wind. The Khalsa attacked the remaining Afgans with so much power that they ran for their lives like headless chickens. The Khalsa claimed complete control of the battlefield. The skies echoed with the battle cry "BOLEH SO NIHAL." Every single Khalsa Lion roared the response "SAT SREE AKAL."

Maharaja Ranjit Singh and General Hari Singh Naluwa looked around at the site of death and destruction, smoke was still emanating from burning crates and bodies. The Akalis told Maharaja Ranjit Singh that by some miracle Guru Gobind Singh himself had caused the explosion. They all knew that they would have suffered a total wipe out against a fanatical Afgan Army on a religious war, armed to the teeth with guns and bullets.

As they wandered around what used to be the camp, Maharaja Ranjit Singh noticed something. Quickly dashing to the outskirts he kneeled down. The others followed him and they con-gregated around the dead body of a young Khalsa woman. She was lying face down on the ground less than fifty feet from the depot and away from the bodies of the Afgans. In her hand she was still tightly clutching a fire torch!

It was the head nurse, Bibi Prem Kaur. This brave lioness, this daughter in spirit of Guru Gobind Singh had given up her life to save the Khalsa Army from a humiliating defeat. While the other nurses retreated with the wounded Akalis, she had secretly gone to the depot and hidden near the bullet storage. Lighting the ammunition, the blast had blown her body away from the dead Afgans, as if to protect her innocence and honour her sacrifice.

This scene deeply moved Maharaja Ranjit Singh and his eyes were filling with tears. Addressing her as his daughter, he gently raised her head onto his lap and tenderly wiped her face with his handkerchief.

The Khalsa warriors witnessed these scenes with tears rolling down their cheeks. Bibi Prem Kaur had sacrificed her own life so that her brothers would be saved. At her funeral the Khalsa Army band played on and the cannons fired in a continuous salute. Maharaja Ranjit Singh and other officers carried her coffin in a royal procession. Every Khalsa warrior felt Bibi Prem Kaur's eternal love for Guru Gobind Singh wash over them. With their heads bowed low, they said great, truly great is our father Guru Gobind Singh Jee.

The amrit-nectar that Guru Gobind Singh had used to transform the sparrows into hawks, jackals into lions, cowards into Khalsa, had now enabled Bibi Prem Kaur to make the ultimate selfless sacrifice. The Khalsa would never forget her. By the Guru's kindness she had single-handedly overturned a sure defeat for the Khalsa into an overwhelming victory.

SHALOK, KABEER:

The battle drum beats
in the sky of the mind;
aim is taken,
and the wound is inflicted.

The spiritual warrior
enters the battlefield (of the mind);
now is the time to fight (against vice)! || 1 ||

The one who fights
in defence of righteousness
is alone known as a warrior.

That one may be cut apart,
piece by piece,
but never leaves
the field of battle. || 2 || 2 ||

Guru Granth Sahib, 1105

DAUGHTER
OF THE
GURU

Based on a true story

"Aren't you afraid Deep Kaur?"

"Afraid of what Sunita?"

"Afraid your husband might not come back?"

Deep Kaur's hands stopped packing the hot chapattis into the white cloth. She looked over the bundle of firewood next to the clay oven she had been cooking at. Sunita's head was peeping over the muddy-brown wall. She wore a grass green scarf, to match her flowery patterned Punjabi suit. It was well worn, even torn in places.

"Sunita you ask too many questions. Everything is in Waheguru's hands."

"Yes, I know you Sikhs believe in accepting God's will. But, as a woman you must worry your husband may not return from battle. I mean when I get married to Ram I'm not going to let him out of my sight."

"Sunita, I think you have talked enough for one

day. Can't you see I'm busy?"

"Why are you packing your food today?   Are you going somewhere?"

Deep Kaur ignored Sunita and finished tying a knot with the corners of the cloth to close the bundle of food.

"You are going somewhere!   O tell me - please! Where are you going?"

"Sunita, I'll only tell you if you promise to keep it a secret."

"You can trust me."

"Today, I am going to have the sacred vision of Guru Gobind Singh.   I have been praying for along time for this moment.   Last night I received a message from my husband in my dream.   He said his group of Sikh soldiers will be passing this way on their journey to Anandpur. I am going to go and meet my husband and meet the beloved Sikhs of my Guru.   I am going to serve them this food and then go with them to meet Guru Gobind Singh.   Sunita, today is a very, very happy day."

"O that's so exciting Deep Kaur.   I wish I had a Guru.   I wish I could come with you. But you know my parents wont even let me out of the house.   Not after what happened to my cousin."

"What happened to her?"

"Yesterday, she had just gone to get a pot of water from the river, when my Uncle heard her screaming.   He saw a Mughal soldier riding off with her on the back of his horse."

"That's terrible!"

"Then my Uncle chased them through the fields, some of the villagers heard him and they managed to scare the horse.   My cousin fell off and the Mughal rode away."

"Is she OK?"

"She got away with a few cuts and bruises.   But

she's having nightmares about the Mughal's face. He had a huge scar from his lip to his ear and he kept trying to kiss her with his yellow teeth and dog breath. She's really worried that the Mughal will come back with more soldiers to get revenge. You know what they're like - and they seem to have hundreds of soldiers roaming this area nowadays."

"Sunita, before I go I want to give you something. You have to promise me you'll keep it with you at all times."

Deep Kaur went inside and returned with a folded piece of gold cloth. She handed it to Sunita.

"Go on, open it."

Sunita carefully unwrapped the cloth to find a beautiful curved piece of wood with a handle coming out of it.

"Thank you Deep Kaur, but I really can't take your knife."

"Call it a kirpan Sunita, a knife is what you cut cucumbers with! This kirpan is a gift from Guru Gobind Singh. With this kirpan you can protect your honour and you can defend your cousin."

"O I can't take a kirpan Deep Kaur. Women aren't supposed to carry things like that."

"What would have happened to your cousin if your Uncle hadn't rescued her?"

Sunita's eyes filled with tears.

"Don't you think it would have been better if your cousin had a kirpan - at least she could have defended herself?"

Sunita took the kirpan and Deep Kaur showed here her how to put it on.

Deep Kaur gave Sunita a quick lesson on how to use it, first Deep Kaur would draw her own kirpan, then Sunita would copy pulling out hers.

"One more thing Sunita, don't think Guru Gobind Singh is just for Sikhs. No, Guru Gobind Singh is there for everyone. So if anything happens to you just pray to Guru Gobind Singh and he will help you. That's what I do."

Deep Kaur stepped forward and hugged Sunita, "You will always be my little sister, but now I have to go. Practise using the kirpan and teach the other girls too, they have to protect themselves."

Deep Kaur wrapped her shawl around a little tighter and strapped the bundle of food and clothes to her back. She walked proud and strong out of the village. She waited where her husband had told to her to, by the biggest tree on the main road. Most of the day had passed. It was gradually getting darker and she was wondering what had happened to the Sikh soldiers.

As the sun set, she began reciting her evening prayer, Rehras Sahib, off by heart. On completing it she felt refreshed and in tune with wonderful Waheguru. Then her heart leapt with joy.

In the distance she saw the silhouettes of six soldiers on horses riding towards her. She got up and ran forward to meet them.

As they approached she caught a glint of their green uniforms. GREEN uniforms! They were not Sikhs they were Mughals!

Deep Kaur darted off the road into the field and hid behind a tree. Her heart was pounding like a drum. She heard the trotting horses going by and the loud voices of the Mughals slowly faded as they passed by. One of the soldiers stopped and shouted to the others he had to go to the toilet. He got off his horse and headed towards the trees. The other soldiers carried on riding forward. Deep Kaur held her breath. She could not run as she would give herself away. The Mughal approached her tree and she saw his face - he had a scar from his lip to his ear. He was the same soldier who tried to kidnap Sunita's cousin.

Deep Kaur's blood started boiling at what he had done. She decided to teach him a lesson. When he took off his sword and squatted down

Bibi Deep Kaur on her way to meet the Guru

she was going to leap out and severely beat him. She calmed herself down saying "Waheguru, Waheguru" under her breath. Standing up with her back pressed against the tree trunk, she waited for him to settle down. Suddenly an arm came swinging around from the side of the tree. Deep Kaur tried to shout, but a hand was pinning her throat against the tree trunk.

Next, she saw Scarface's yellow teeth lunging at her. She tried to kick back, but it was too late his full body weight was pressing down on her. With one hand she tried to push back his face, while the other hand pulled out her kirpan. She couldn't move her arm to swing the kirpan and now started feeling dizzy. Everything was going black. As she tried to give him one last push, they both tumbled to the ground. He landed on top of her and let out a grunt. Blood trickled out of the corner of his mouth, and his body went limp. Deep Kaur pushed him off and looked at her kirpan - it was sticking out of his chest. He had fallen on it.

The sun had set, it was almost pitch black. She heard the other Mughal soldiers calling out for

Scarface, "Khan! Khan! Where are you."

Deep Kaur pulled out her kirpan and cleaned off the blood. She scrambled through the bushes back to the road. In the distance she could hear the sounds of more horses heading down the road. Behind her she could hear the soldiers searching. Where could she go? One of the soldiers spotted her and all five came scrambling up the roadside verge. Deep Kaur looked death in the face and charged at them with her kirpan. In her mind, she remembered Guru Gobind Singh's words, '..may I die fighting ...'

From behind her she heard the Sikh battle cry 'Bolay So Nihal - Sat Sree Akal.' It gave her a new burst of life. She looked back and the Sikh soldiers had arrived waving the flag, wearing the blue uniform and tall turban. She looked forward and the Mughals had mounted their horses and raced away. Bibi Deep Kaur fell to the ground totally exhausted.

When she woke up, her husband was giving her sips of water. He greeted her and told her they had brought her to the city of the Guru,

Anandpur.

From behind him, a beautiful voice was heard asking, "Where is she?" Her husband stepped aside and the handsome warrior Guru Gobind Singh stepped forward.

His radiant face showered love and blessings on Deep Kaur. She humbly looked down at her Guru's feet. She tried to speak, but her throat was too sore. Guru Gobind Singh smiled, "This is my Daughter. My brave daughter! With warriors like you the Khalsa will remain in high spirits."

"I am honoured
because of the Khalsa ...
The Khalsa is
my brave friend"

Guru Gobind Singh

HAIL TO THE SWORD!

The sword (the power of God) slashes well.
It cuts the army of foolish people into pieces.
It is so powerful that it makes
the battlefield beautiful.

It is an unbreakable hand weapon,
it is of great splendour.
Its brightness puts the brightness
of the sun to shame.

It brings peace and joy to saints.
It crushes evil intellect.
It destroys sins and
I am in its refuge.

Hail! Hail! to the Creator,
the saviour of the world,
my cherisher.
Hail to the sword,
the power of God.

Guru Gobind Singh,
Bachittar Natak.

GLOSSARY

Akalis
Brave battalion of the Khalsa Army.

Akali Phoola Singh
Born in 1761, died in battle in 1823. He never married, but settled in Amritsar. A fierce and selfless warrior, he was loved and feared at the same time. He became honorary Jathedar of the Akal Takhat.

Amrit
Holy water prepared in an iron bowl and stirred by the double-edged sword in the Sikh initiation ceremony.

Bhagat
Saint

Bolay So Nihal, Sat Sree Akal
Sikh battle-cry. Meaning "Whoever speaks it will be Joyous :God Is True"

Chakr
Circular blade worn around the Sikh warrior's turban and thrown like a discus.

Emperor Aurangzeb
One of the last Emperors of the Mughal Dynasty. He reigned from 1658 to 1707. He promoted aggressive conversions to Islam.

Guru
Spiritual Enlightener.

Guru Gobind Singh Jee
Tenth Master of the Sikhs. Destroyed tyrants defended

saints.

Guru Granth Sahib Jee
Sikh holy scriptures - the living Guru of the Sikhs.

Jathedar
Leader of a group of Sikhs.

Jee
"Jee" after a person's name shows respect.

Karta Purakh
God - 'The Creative Being'

Khalsa
1.An initiated Sikh,
2. The Sikh Army created in 1699

Khalsa Raj
Sikh Kingdom

Khanda
Double-edged sword.

Maharaja Ranjit Singh
Great Ruler of the Sikh Kingdom. Also known as Shera Punjab - 'Lion of Punjab'

Mughal
The Mughal Dynasty was a line of Muslim emperors who reigned India from 1526 to 1858.

Waheguru
God - 'The Wonderful Being who takes us from Darkness to Light'.

Waheguru Jee Ka Khalsa,
Waheguru Jee Kee Fateh
Sikh Greeting - 'Waheguru's Khalsa, Waheguru's Victory'

ABOUT THE AUTHOR
Harjit Singh

I have been blessed with serving the Guru's children by running workshops. I am married to Davinder Kaur and we have a daughter, HarSimran. When I see her, I know Waheguru has given me a mission to make as many inspiring books for the next generation.

Website : www.Sikh-Heroes.com
Email : Harjit@sikh-heroes.com
To get inspiring emails join my newsgroup:
SpiritBornPeople-subscribe@yahoogroups.com

ACKNOWLEDGMENTS

On my travels Waheguru has crossed my path with many talented Sikhs, great appreciation goes to Harjit Singh "Artist" for the wonderful artwork and Taranjit Singh for all the professional design work and the original website.

I would also like to thank Baldev Singh for the translations from "Ardashak Singhnia" by Karam Singh (published by Niranjan Singh & Sons, Amritsar, 1981).

I am grateful to the sevadars who made "Gurbani CD" and "Shabad Keertan" by Dr Santokh Singh for the English translations of the Guru's words. The ultimate thanks go to Wondrous God - Waheguru who made this whole project possible.

Email Harjit Singh "Artist" :
Harjit39@hotmail.com

Email Taranjit Singh :
Taran0@yahoo.com

GET YOUR FREE POSTER

Did you like the cover artwork and the website? Would you like to have your own fantastic copy of this great poster for your bedroom wall or local Gurdwara or school? Well here's your chance to get it free. All you have to pay for is £2 to cover the costs of postage and packing.

THE ACTUAL POSTER IS A2 FULL COLOUR.

TO APPLY : Complete your details below (or copy this page) and send it with £2 for postage & packing to: www.Sikh-Heroes.com, 26 Rondini Avenue, Luton, Beds, LU3 1RR. Cheques should be made out to 'www.sikh-heroes.com.' **This offer only applies to the UK.**

Please send a fantastic colour A2 size poster to

Name :_____

Address : _____

_____

_____

Post Code : _____

Country :   UK

Email Address: _____